The T'ai Chi Companion

by David-Dorian Ross

Vol. I:

The Short Form Workbook

Contents

How to Use this Book

The T'ai Chi Companion series is designed to be your personal workbook for self-study. In other words, you can use this as your text for the classes you are taking from an instructor, or you can use it to study in the comfort and privacy of your home environment. The workbook exercises can be done again and again. We recommend students use Volume One for the first six months of their study.

Every lesson is followed by a series of simple exercises to help reinforce the lesson. It's not always enough to just follow the steps of each movement. The essence of practice is to experiment with what you learn. Try it in a variety of ways. Do it differently from the way your teacher presents it. Do it backwards; do it wrong. Play with the timing, and continually ask yourself the question: "What would happen if I did *this*?"

Every practice session or classroom experience creates an opportunity for you to learn something about your T'ai Chi, and consequently, about yourself. Keeping a journal of these experiences is an invaluable technique for remembering and then actualizing what your learn in these sessions. If you're not used to keeping a journal, however, sometimes you may find yourself not quite sure how to express your experiences. Each lesson, therefore, includes a place for you to enter some specific notes in a format used by many athletes on the US Olympic team. This format is called Performance Analysis, and I've used it for almost ten years -- it helped me get to the World Championships twice. It also helped me keep the notes that eventually became my book The Ultimate Exercise.

Performance Analysis has three parts: Solution Analysis, Success Analysis and Knowledge Analysis. When you make entries into your workbook, simply follow the format of these three sections.

Solution Analysis helps you solve recurring problems. For example, suppose you consistently lose your balance trying to step into a T-step in the transition between each step of Part Horses Mane. As you experiment with solutions during your practice sessions, write your problem, then your ideas about how to solve them under Solution Analysis. Finally, write a first person, present tense statement providing a solution. For example: "When I step up to a T-step, I relax and turn my waist. I keep my balance every time."

Success Analysis helps you focus on the things that go right instead of the things that go wrong. Always concentrate on your successes, rather than your failures. Under Success Analysis, write something positive about what you did in practice or class today. Sometimes, this might just be the note, "Well, I made it through a whole hour of practice!"

Knowledge Analysis is the place to record new discoveries. Each practice session, work-out or competition provides lessons. Each time you do your T'ai Chi lesson, ask yourself, "What did I learn new today?"

One last note. The only secret to mastering the art of T'ai Chi Ch'uan is to practice. Practice a little every day -- even it's only five minutes. Like the Chinese say, "One step at a time, you can climb all the way to Heaven."

Six Basic Principles

As you begin to learn the movements of the T'ai Chi routines, you should also learn the basic principles which guide the spirit of the movements. These basic principles underscore each movement, providing you with guidelines as to how the movements are supposed to be performed. Here is the list of Six Basic Principles which you should learn along with your first Yang Style form.

1. The Movements must be done Slowly.

2. Relax your body.

3. Let the motions be simple and easy: flow with the body's "Natural" way of moving.

4. Bend your knees and Sink Down. (Remember, it doesn't matter how low you sink down, but whatever level you do sink to, you must stay at that level until the end of the routine.)

5. Make your movements Continuous from beginning to end.

6. Let your movements exhibit a balance between Yin and Yang.

Of course, a list of principles like this needs more explanation. Have fun experimenting with exploring both principles and movements on your own, but when the time is right, find a teacher for personal instruction.

Lesson One

The

Basic
Positions

The Basic Positions

If you scan through the diagrams in this workbook, you'll notice that there are a lot more than 24 movements!

This is because, although we call this the 24-*movement* form, a better translation might be "24 individual martial arts techniques." Some of the techniques have multiple steps, and all the techniques are connected by slowly flowing transitional movements. So all together there are about 175 different transitional movements and postures in this routine. Yet all of these different moves are based on a very small number of fundamental positions of the hands and feet. Once you learn these basic positions, you can do almost all the movements in the whole form.

The first basic foot position is called the "Bow and Arrow Step," or Bow Step, for short. This is a lunge position in which the front leg is bent, like the bow, and the back leg is fairly straight, like the arrow. In this position, 70% of your weight is over the front leg, and only 30% of your weight is over the back leg. Step forward with the left foot so that the front knee is bent and the weight shifts forward 70%. In Yang style T'ai Chi — which is the style you'll study in this workbook — the front toe points directly forward toward your direction of travel. The back foot adjusts forward by pivoting on the heel, until the toe points at about a 45° angle. Each and every time you change your bow step, you must do these two things: 1) Bend your front knee and shift the weight forward 70%, and 2) adjust the back foot.

"Bow and Arrow Step,"

6

The second basic foot position is called the 'T-Step'. In this position you are basically standing on one foot, while the other foot just touches the floor next to your supporting leg. From the side that this position looks like a "T".

"T-Step"

The last basic foot position is called the "Empty step." The Empty step is just like the T-step, except that this time the un-weighted foot is out in front of the supporting leg (about shoulder width). In the Empty step, both knees are bent, and the empty foot turns in just slightly towards the center-line of the body. This position is called the Empty step because the front foot is 'empty,' or devoid of weight. You should be able to pick your front foot up off the ground without having to first shift your weight to the back foot.

"Empty step"

Here is one more basic position. This a basic position of the hands is traditionally called, "Embracing the Moon," although we usually just call it "Holding the Ball" — since that's what it looks like. Make a circle with your hands just like you were holding a big beach ball in front of your body. The top arm comes right across your chest, while the bottom arm comes across your hips. The top wrist is relaxed, the top elbow is angled downward and the bottom hand is cupped upward, just as if it were conforming to the circular configuration of the ball. You can make the Hold the Ball posture with either hand on top.

"Embracing the Moon"

So those are your basic positions: Bow step, T-step, Empty step plus Hold the Ball. These basic positions will form the foundations of more than 80% of the whole short form.

Open the Door

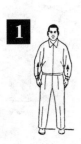

B egin by standing with your feet together, hands relaxed at your sides. The head is held erect and the eyes look out slightly above the horizon, with an open focus. The body is held with the spine in neutral alignment -- relaxed, not stiff, but not slouched either. This is what we call the T'ai Chi Position -- the moment of stillness before movement begins. The direction you are facing in the T'ai Chi Position we will designate as 12 o'clock, and for the rest of the routine this will be the 'front' position

1. Slowly step to the left with the left foot about shoulder width, and center your weight evenly over both feet.

2. Slowly raise both hands to chest height.

3. Now bend both knees and sink down as though you were sitting down on a chair.

4. In the final posture, both knees are bent, both elbows are slightly bent, the palms face down towards the floor. The head is held erect, but the spinal alignment is neutral. Avoid sticking your chest or butt out.

MOVEMENT TWO
Parting the Horse's Mane

Part Horse's Mane involves three steps, or three final postures, created by forming a Bow step and extending one hand out while withdrawing the other hand to the hip. The steps zigzag to alternating corners: 8 o'clock with the left hand out, then 10 o'clock with the right hand out, then 8 o'clock with the left hand out again.

1. Shift the weight over the right foot and step in T-step with the left foot.

2. Simultaneously, form a hold the ball position, right hand on top. Remember that right now you are still facing 12 o'clock with your weight on the right foot.

3. With the left foot, step diagonally into the 8 o'clock corner, and turn left to create a Bow step.

4. Next, extend the left hand (palm up) in a diagonal line from hip to shoulder level, and withdraw the right hand down to the right hip, palm down. In the final position, your elbows are both slightly bent, and the left palm is turned up at a diagonal angle.

5. After the first Part Horse's Mane, rock back, lifting the left toe, and then pivot the foot on the heel toward the left until it faces six o'clock.

6. Shift the weight forward and step up onto the left foot, making a T-step with the right foot. All the weight is now on the left foot.

7. As you step up into your T-step, fold your hands in to hold the ball, this time left hand on top.

8. Step diagonally into the 10 o'clock corner, creating a Bow step with the right foot forward.

9. As you step forward, extend the right hand, palm up, and withdraw the left hand to the left hip, palm down.

10. Now rock back again, shifting your weight onto the left foot and lifting the right toes.

11. Pivoting on the right heel, turn that foot toward the right until it faces 12 o'clock.

12. Shift the weight forward, step up onto the right foot and create a T-step with the left foot. Now you are back to facing your original position, 12 o'clock. Simultaneously hold the ball, right hand on top.

13. The last step is the same as the first. Step diagonally to the 8 o'clock corner, shift and turn into a Bow step.

14. At the same time, extend the left hand, palm up, and withdraw the right hand to the right hip, palm down.

Exercises

1. In the first lesson, you were introduced to several fundamental foot positions, or "stances," as they are called. So far, you have used the Bow step and the T-step. Coming up in the next lesson, you'll be using the Empty step, and later on, the Crouch step. For now, practice the Bow step, T-step and Empty step. Form each stance 10 times on each leg, and hold each stance for 5 seconds before you relax.

Question: Can you describe to someone else how to make a Bow step, T-step or Empty step? How about Embracing the Moon ("holding the ball" posture)? Make some notes below.

2. Experiment with the timing your motion so the left hand reaches its final position at the exact moment that your legs finish their Bow step. The fun and challenging part of learning T'ai Chi is coordinating the hands and feet together. Actually, all the movements should begin at the same moment and end at the same moment -- "in one breath," as the T'ai Chi Classics say. After you step out, the shift and turn into a Bow step, the movement of the left hand and the movement of the right hand are all simultaneous. Make some notes below.

Practice Notes & Performance Analysis

I. Solution Analysis:
Write a <u>first person, present tense</u> statement providing a solution.

II. Success Analysis:
Write something positive about what you did in practice or class today.

III. Knowledge Analysis:
"What did I learn <u>new</u> today?"

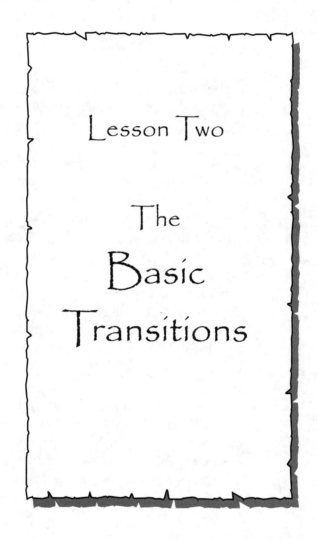

Lesson Two

The

Basic

Transitions

White Crane Spreads Wings

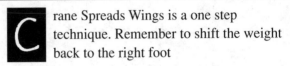

C rane Spreads Wings is a one step technique. Remember to shift the weight back to the right foot

1. As you complete Part Horse's Mane's third Bow step, shift your weight forward onto the left foot and step in a half-step with the right foot. Now, shift all your weight back onto the right leg, which will create an Empty step.

2. As you shift your weight back onto the right foot, form a hold-ball posture with the left hand on top. Lift the right hand skyward (about nose high) and withdraw the left hand to the left hip. Remember: The technique of Crane Spreads Wings is to separate the hands vertically.

3. Allow your waist to turn to the right, then back to center again. The waist turn is a small movement, about 1/4 turn. In the final position, face 9 o'clock, and place the left toe in front of you on the nine o'clock line.

Brush Knee and Push

T he footwork in this movement is exactly like the footwork in Part Horse's Mane. Brush Knee and push involves three steps, or three final postures, created by forming a Bow step and pushing with the opposite side hand out while withdrawing the other hand to the hip. The steps zig-zag to alternating corners: 8 o'clock with the right hand pushing, then 10 o'clock with the left hand pushing, then 8 o'clock with the right hand pushing again.

1. From the end of Crane Spreads Wings,

2. Drop the right hand downward, turn the waist, look over to the right. Bring both arms over to the right, simultaneously relax the right hand, and let it sweep in a downward arc until it has swept all the way down and up again to the right shoulder. At the same time, lift the left hand and sweep it in an overhead (nose height, really) arc, also towards the right.

3. In the final position, you should be facing 12 o'clock, with both hands extending to the right, just a shoulder level. Right hand palm is up and left hand palm down.

4. With the left foot, step diagonally to 8 o'clock to make a Bow step. As you step, bend the right elbow, drawing the right hand in past the ear and then extending it forward, pushing with the palm.

5. In the final position, the left hand first presses down, then sweeps around the knee, ending up at the left hip, palm down -- just like in Part Horse's Mane.

6. From the end of the first Brush Knee and Push position, rock back, lifting the left toe and turn to the left until it faces 6 o'clock.

7. Shift the weight forward onto the left foot, and step up with the right foot, creating a T-step. At the same the hands circle towards the left in a mirror image of the first transition. The left hand sweeps in a downward arc towards the left, and the right hand sweeps overhead in another arc, also to the left.

8. In the final position, you should be facing 6 o'clock in a T-step with both arms extending towards the left, left hand palm up and right hand palm down.

9. With the right foot, step diagonally to the 10 o'clock corner. As you step, bend the left elbow, drawing the left hand in past the ear, and then extending it forward, pushing with the palm.

10. Shift your weight forward to create a Bow step. Simultaneously, the right hand presses down to brush around the knee and then back to the hip.

11. Rock back, lifting the right toes and turning them to the right until they face 12 o'clock.

12. Shift the weight forward onto the right foot and step up with the left foot, T-step.

13. Gently circle both arms to the right as you did in the first part of this movement. Now you are back in your original position, facing 12 o'clock.

14. The last step is the same as the first. With the left foot, step diagonally to the 8 o'clock corner.

15. Shift your weight forward into a Bow step, while the right hand brushes past the ear and pushes forward and the left hand brushes around the knee and then withdraws to the left hip, palm down.

Exercises

1. In the second lesson, you had a chance to observe that the movement in T'ai Chi comes from the motions that get you from one final posture to the next. We call these "the Basic Transitions." So far, you have used the "simple step-in, T-step," "rock back, rock forward to a T-step," and "the Empty-step change" transitions. Later on, you'll learn the "double weight-shift" and the "Crouch step change" transition. For now, practice the "simple step-in, T-step," "rock back, rock forward to a T-step," and "the Empty-step change" transitions. Perform each transition 10 times.

Question: Can you describe to someone else how to get from the end of Part Horse's Mane to Crane Spreads Wings? How about from one Brush Knee posture to the next? Make some notes below.

2. One of the most confusing parts of Brush Knee is coordinating the left hand with the right hand with the waist turn with the step... there's a lot of movement happening all at once. But if you can just get the initial phase of the movement, the rest will just fall into place. Basically, there are three parts to this phase. 1) The waist is beginning it's turn to the corner, 2) then the right hand curls into the ear, and 3) the left hand pushes all the way down the length of the torso.

Try this exercise, adding each piece one by one. First, turn the waist... and then turn back. Next, turn waist and push the left hand down... and turn back. Finally, turn waist, push the left palm down, and curl right hand into the ear... and turn back. When you put all these together, it kind of looks like you're directing traffic, so this is called this the 'Traffic Cop Drill.' Just do the turn, left hand push down, right hand into the ear, and then turn back. Do ten repetitions of these on each foot, and on the final repetition, complete the movement and step to the corner for Brush Knee & Push.

Practice Notes & Performance Analysis

I. Solution Analysis:

Write a <u>first person, present tense</u> statement providing a solution.

II. Success Analysis:

Write something positive about what you did in practice or class today.

III. Knowledge Analysis:

"What did I learn <u>new</u> today?"

Lesson Three

The

First two
Principles

The first two basic principles

The first basic principle of T'ai Chi is **Slow Down**. Perhaps the most distinctive characteristic of T'ai Chi is the fact that the movements are done so slowly. There are many reasons for this, but there are two you should be aware of as beginners. First, the incredibly slow pace forces you to focus your attention on the precision of the movements. And second, the repeated slow movements through each limb's range of motion forces open and then strengthens the neuromuscular pathways which give you greater muscular control. In other words, there is both a mental and physical reason for the slow movement.

The second basic principle is **Relax.** After the slow tempo of the movements, the next characteristic an observer is likely to notice is the graceful and relaxed quality of T'ai Chi movements. A good T'ai Chi player will exhibit inner strength and control and at the same time will seem to flow like water. You can do it too by practicing the second principle of T'ai Chi — relax the body! The essence of this principle is learning to identify the muscles needed for an activity as opposed to the ones not needed, and then memorizing the *difference* between the two. In technical terms we can call this "differential relaxation."

MOVEMENT FIVE
Play the Pi'pa

The footwork in this movement, complete with waist turn and foot replacement, is exactly the same as it was in Crane Spreads Wings. The only difference comes at the replacement: this time you replace your left foot heel down, toe up.

1. From the last position in Brush Knee and Push, step up one-half step with the right foot and slowly bring the left hand forward.

2. Immediately shift the weight back onto the right foot, creating an Empty step. Simultaneously, turn the waist toward the right, and then turn back to the left.

3. As you turn back, squeeze the open palm of the right hand just underneath the left elbow. Replace the left foot onto floor, heel down and toe up. In the final position, face toward 9 o'clock.

Step Back, Repulse Monkey

When you "Step Back to Repulse the Monkey", you retreat with a continuous series of Empty steps -- six of them, to be exact, ending with the weight on the right foot and the left foot "empty."

1. From the final position of Play Pi'pa, turn the right palm up, and at the same time turn the waist to the right and sweep the right hand down past the thigh in a large downward arc.

2. Continue the arc until the right hand extends all the way behind you to the right corner, palm up, reaching out the shoulder.

3. Turning the waist back to the left, curl in the fingers, then wrist and elbow to bring the right palm past the cheek, and then push it forward (just like Brush Knee). As the palm comes past the cheek, simultaneously step back with the left foot a normal walking backwards pace.

4. Shift the weight entirely onto the left foot, creating a new Empty step with the right foot forward. Now you should be facing 9 o'clock, pushing out with the right palm, and the left palm withdrawn to the left hip, palm up. *You have just completed <u>one</u> step.*

26

5. Continue the the motion by turning the waist to the left and sweeping the left hand down past the thigh in a large downward arc. Continue the arc until the left habnd extentd all the waty behind you to the left corner, palm up, reaching out from the shoulder.

6. Turning the waist back to the right, curl the fingers, then the wrist and elbow to bring the left palm past the cheek, and then push it forward (just like in the first step). As the palm comes past the cheek, simultaneously step back with the right foot in a normal walking backwards pace.

7. Shift the weight entirely onto the right foot, creating a new Empty step with the left foot forward. Now you should be facing 9 o'clock, pushing out with the left palm, and the right palm withdrawn to the left hip, palm up. *You have just completed two step.*

Continue stepping in this pattern until you have completed six steps, finishin in an Empty step facing 9 o'clock, with the left foot in front and the left palm pushing outwards.

Exercises

1. Now that you've learned the entire first section of the Short Form, you should begin to pay attention the basic principles which guide the way these movements are performed. Read over the first two principles, and then go practice your form, concentrating on these guidelines.

The first principle is "Slow Down." At a normal tempo, the Short form should take approximately five to ten minutes to complete. A good rule of thumb, however, is that however slow you think you should be going, you could always go a little slower.

The second principle is "Relax." Little by little, T'ai Chi encourages you to release the tension in your body. Try this exercise: every movement you make, pretend you are balancing a balloon in the palm of your hand. If you move too quickly, the balloon will blow away; if your hands and arms are too tense, the balloon will pop.

Try these principles out when you practice, and then make some notes below.

2. Beginning students often have trouble keeping their balance in Step Back, Repulse Monkey. If you find you have this trouble, it may be because you are crossing your feet when you step back.

Practice the footwork only, stepping back and creating Empty steps. Take care to step past the supporting foot, and *then diagonally backwards*.

Next, practice the footwork and add the waist turn with every step. After you have performed three lines of the footwork, add the hand motions.

Practice Notes & Performance Analysis

I. Solution Analysis:

Write a <u>first person, present tense</u> statement providing a solution.

II. Success Analysis:

Write something positive about what you did in practice or class today.

III. Knowledge Analysis:

"What did I learn <u>new</u> today?"

Lesson Four

The

Double
Weight Shift

The Third basic principle

The third basic principle is the principle of **Natural Motion.** T'ai Chi Ch'uan is part of the family of martial arts traditionally called "internal martial arts." The term "internal" refers to the idea that in T'ai Chi Ch'uan the strength comes from the inner life energy, rather than from the outer, external muscles. These are two completely different kinds of strength. In Chinese, physical, muscular strength is called *li*, while the internal energy is called *ch'i*. Of course, in T'ai Chi Ch'uan, we trying to develop our ch'i, and to learn how to let it flow from the inside out. It is no accident, then, that the very movements of T'ai Chi Ch'uan should seem to flow from the inside out, just like walking. This idea is expressed by the third basic principle: The Movements Should Be Natural. Another way of expressing this principle is that the movements should be simple or easy. None of the movements or postures we will learn in this routine should ever make you feel strained or uncomfortable. If you ever feel like you have to tie yourself up into a pretzel to do a movement, then you're probably making too much out of the posture.

Grasp the Bird's Tail-left

1. Turn to the right to face 12 o'clock again. Remember that your weight remains on the right foot during the transition.

2. Bring the left foot over to form the T-step.

3. As you step in, form a hold the ball posture with the right hand on top.

4. With the left foot, step diagonally towards 8 o'clock with the left foot, creating a Bow step.

5. Simultaneously extend the rounded left arm forward towards 9 o'clock so that the palm is cupped, facing you and with the thumb generally pointing up to heaven. This is what we call Ward-off position. At the same time, withdraw the right hand to the right hip, palm facing down.

6. Turn the left palm down and the right palm up, and reach forward with the right hand until both palms are parallel, right palm near left elbow.

7. Now turn the waist to the right, and shift the weight so that 60% is over the right foot. At the same time, pull both hands in a downward arc over to the 2 o'clock corner. This is the technique known as "Roll-back."

8. Turn left until you face 9 o'clock. Change the position of the hands, rounding the left arm and placing the right palm across the left wrist.

9. Now push with the right palm and shift the weight forward until you are in a Bow step. As you complete your turn and push, you will look just like you are doing Ward-off, only with extra strength. This is the part of Grasp the Bird's Tail known as Press.

10. Slide the right palm over the left wrist and then separate the hands to approximately shoulder width.

11. Rock back, shifting the body weight over the right leg, and lift the left toe as you do so.

12. Simultaneously, withdraw both palms in and down toward your belly button.

13. Rock your weight forward until you re-form a Bow step. As you rock forward, curve both arms upward and forward. This is the final phase of Grasp the Bird's Tail, the technique known as Push.

TRANSITION:

The Double Weight Shift

---

1. At the end of Push, relax both hands so that the palms face the floor.

2. Letting the hands just float, turn right and shift your weight to the right leg. This will allow you to pivot on the left heel and turn your left toes to 12 o'clock.

3. Let the right hand drop down a little.

4. Now shift your weight back to the left foot and step in with the right foot, T-step. At the very end, as you make that T-step, fold your hands in to hold the ball, left hand on top.

Grasp the Bird's Tail-right

A fter your double weight shift, form T-step transition, you should be facing 12 o'clock with the left hand on top.

1. Step diagonally to 4 o'clock, creating a Bow step.

2. As you step, simultaneously lift the rounded right arm towards 3 o'clock so that the palm is cupped, facing you and with the thumb generally pointing up to heaven. With draw the left hand to the left hip, palm facing down.

3. Turn the right palm down and the left palm up, and reach forward with the left hand until both palms are parallel, left palm near right elbow.

4. Now shift the weight to the left foot and turn at the waist to the left. Simultaneously, pull both hands in a downward arc over to the 10 o'clock corner.

5. Turn at the waist back to the right until you face 3  o'clock. Change the position of the hands, placing the left palm across the right wrist. Now push with the left palm and shift the weight forward until you are in a Bow step. As you complete your turn and push, you will look just like you are doing Ward-off, only with extra strength.

6. Slide the left palm over the right wrist and then  separate the hands to approximately shoulder width.

7. Rock back, shifting the body weight over  the left leg, and lift the right toe.

8. Simultaneously, withdraw both palms in and  down toward your belly button.

9. Rock your weight forward until you re-form a  Bow step. As you rock forward, curve both arms upward and forward.

Single Whip

1

1. From the end of Grasping the Bird's Tail, sit back to shift the weight to the left foot, lifting the right toes. Turn the right palm to face you, and sweep the left hand in an arc downward to face in towards your abdomen.

2

2. Hold your hands in this position as you turn and shift to the left foot. Before you shift back to the right foot, reverse your hold the ball position, right hand on top with the right palm facing you.

3

3. Now, holding your hands in this position, shift back to the right foot and step in T-step.

There is just one step in this movement's footwork.

4

4. Step in T-step, with the weight on the right foot. At the same time, form a hook with the right handm, allow the left hand to sweep upwards to the right shoulder height. (the hook hand is created by bringing all the fingers together at the thumb, and then bending the wrist.)

5. From the T-step created at the end of your transition, step diagonally with the left foot to the 8 o'clock corner to make a Bow step. Here's what the hands do: As you step in with the left foot to form a T-step, the right hand turns palm down at 2 o'clock to form a hook hand. The hook hand is created by brining all the fingers together at the thumb and then bending the wrist. While the right hand is making the hook, the left hand circles up to the right wrist.

5. As you step into your bow step, the left hand sweeps across the face (a blocking maneuver) and turns the palm acing out and pushes out a little (a palm strike maneuver). n the final position, the left palm is facing out to 9 o'clock, ut the hook hand is still hooked in the 2 o'clock corner.

Exercises

1. The third basic principle is the principle of Natural Motion, which implies that you should *allow* your body to perform the T'ai Chi movements, rather than *force* your body to do the T'ai Chi movements. Another way of expressing this is that the movements should be simple and easy.

Question: Which of the movements you've learned so far is the most difficult? Go back to that movement and break it apart. Review the instructions in the diagram manual. Experiment, and see if there is some way to make this movement simpler, and more natural feeling. Make some notes below.

2. In this lesson, you've learned a new basic transition: the Double Weight Shift. This transition is used every time you want to turn around 180 degrees.

To correctly perform the Double Weight Shift transition, you must remember three criteria. 1) Rock back first before turning, 2)Turn the waist all the way to the right or left before turning back, 3) shift the weigh *all the way* onto the right or left foot before shifting back, and 4) simultaneously with the first turn and weight shift, turn the back toes (left toes when you turn right, right toes if you're turning left) to face the front. When the toes come down, don't let them turn out again! Leave them facing forward, and this will make your eventual turn around smooth and natural.

Practice the Double weight shift 5 times in both directions. Stand in a Bow step facing left, with the left foot forward. Double weight shift to the right. Finish in a Bow step facing right with the right foot forward. Repeat, going the other direction. Make some notes below.

Practice Notes & Performance Analysis

I. Solution Analysis:
Write a <u>first person, present tense</u> statement providing a solution.

II. Success Analysis:
Write something positive about what you did in practice or class today.

III. Knowledge Analysis:
"What did I learn <u>new</u> today?"

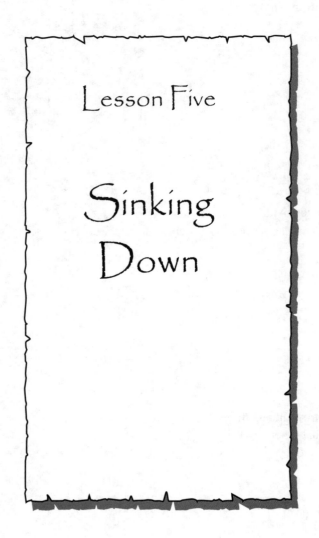

Lesson Five

Sinking Down

The fourth basic principle

The fourth basic principle is the principle of **Sinking Down**. You will notice that from the very first movement of the routine, you lower your body weight by bending your knees, and then maintain this posture until the end of the routine! This is what we call 'sinking.' When you sink down, you are lowering the center of gravity closer to the base, increasing your stability. You also begin to build up the muscular strength of your thighs. In ancient China, they were ignorant of the principles of modern isotonic weight training. They didn't have Microfit or Nautilus machines. But they did discover that if you remove the biomechanical advantage of standing erect, and then try to move around, the leg muscles have to work overtime. Another important meaning of the word "sink" is to relax, and drop (or sink) you chi down into the tant'ien, a point just below your belly button.

Wave Hands Like Clouds

Wave Hands Like Clouds is a beautiful and gentle movement that consists of a series of circular blocking motions that protect the face. The blocks, both left and right, coincide with the turn of the body from left to right, etc. One hint will help you: all the steps go to the left. The left foot always steps out to the left, and the right foot always comes over to the left to form a T-step.

1. To get from the end of Single Whip to this next movement, we're going to use a variation of the double weight shift. Sit back shift your weight onto right leg (turn your body to the right).

2. Pivot on the heel and turn the left toes to 12 o'clock.

3. Release the hook, and bring the left hand, palm facing you, up to shoulder height

4. Drop the right hand down to a position in front of the abdomen, palm facing inward. Shift back to the left foot as the first of a series of sideways shuffle steps. (The footwork in this movement is a series of sideways shuffle steps, and the good news is that all the steps go to the left).

5. Step together with the right foot. Now exchange the hand positions, raising the right hand and dropping the left.

6. Turn the waist to the right, subtly shifting the weight to the right foot.

7. As the waist turns, carry the hands to the right side. By the way this completes the first "Wave Hands Like Clouds" (WHLC).

8. To start the second WHLC step, step sideways with the left foot, and simultaneously exchange the hands, raising the left palm and dropping the right.

9. Drop the right hand down to a position in front of the abdomen, palm facing inward. Shift back to the left foot as the first of a series of sideways shuffle steps. (The footwork in this movement is a series of sideways shuffle steps, and the good news is that all the steps go to the left).

10. Step together with the right foot. Now exchange the hand positions, raising the right hand and dropping the left.

11. Turn the waist to the right, subtly shifting the weight to the right foot.

12. As the waist turns, carry the hands to the right side. By the way this completes the second "Wave Hands Like Clouds" (WHLC).

13. To start the third WHLC step, step sideways with the left foot, and simultaneously exchange the hands, raising the left palm and dropping the right.

14. Drop the right hand down to a position in front of the abdomen, palm facing inward. Shift back to the left foot as the first of a series of sideways shuffle steps. (The footwork in this movement is a series of sideways shuffle steps, and the good news is that all the steps go to the left).

15. Step together with the right foot. Now exchange the hand positions, raising the right hand and dropping the left.

16. Turn the waist to the right, subtly shifting the weight to the right foot.

17. As the waist turns, carry the hands to the right side. This completes the third and final "Wave Hands Like Clouds" (WHLC).

MOVEMENT ELEVEN
Single Whip

As you complete the third step of Wave Hands Like Clouds, your weight will be on the right foot and you will be facing 2 o'clock.

1. Instead of jchanging the hands, just turn the right palm down at 2 o'clock to form a hook hand. While the right hand is making the hook, the left hand circles up to the right wrist.

2. Step diagonally with the left foot to 8 o'clock to create a Bow step. The left hand sweeps across the face (a blocking maneuver), turns the palm to face outward and pushes out a little (a palm strike maneuver).

3. In the final position, the left palm is facing out to 9 o'clock, but the hook hand is still hooked in the 2 o'clock corner.

High Pat on Horse

To get from the end of the second Single Whip to this next position, you will use the Empty step change transition. Unlike before, however, this time you are already facing straight ahead. Therefore, the replacement at the end puts the left foot into the corner, facing 8 o'clock.

1. Take half a step forward with right foot and then shift weight to right leg, forming an empty step. As you step up, open right hand and supinate both palms.

2. Turn your body slightly to the left and curl the right hand in past the right ear and push it forward. Withdraw the left hand to the left hip, palm still facing upward. Meanwhile, replace the left toe towards the 8 o'clock corner.

Exercises

1. The fourth principle turns your T'ai Chi Ch'uan routine into a challenging physical workout. It's the principle of "Sinking Down." T'ai Chi Ch'uan authorities talk about the three 'levels' of T'ai Chi -- low, medium and high. These three levels refer to how much you bend your knees, which will bring you to a high, medium or low level. Now, it doesn't matter which level you sink to. In fact, you might only bend your knees slightly when you sink down. What is important, however, is that whatever level you sink to, *stay at that level until the end of the routine!*

Exercise: Practice a movement you know well -- Part Horse's Mane, for example. First sink down a little bit to a "high" level, and practice this movement for eight to ten steps. Next try this at the "medium" level, and then again at the "low" level. Make some notes below.

2. The T'ai Chi Classics repeatedly remind us that the correct way to move is to "relax, and turn the waist." It's the waist turn that carry the limbs into their final positions, rather than bending and reaching with the arms and hands. Wave hands like clouds is an excellent example of a movement that should focus on the waist turn.

Question: Do you have trouble coordinating the arms and legs in Wave Hands Like Clouds? It may be because you're trying to use too much hand motion. Try it without the feet, like this: place your hands in the Wave Hands position. Now leave them alone; don't move them. Turn the waist. Now change the hands. Turn the waist. That's Wave Hands Like Clouds.

Practice Notes & Performance Analysis

I. Solution Analysis:
Write a <u>first person, present tense</u> statement providing a solution.

II. Success Analysis:
Write something positive about what you did in practice or class today.

III. Knowledge Analysis:
"What did I learn <u>new</u> today?"

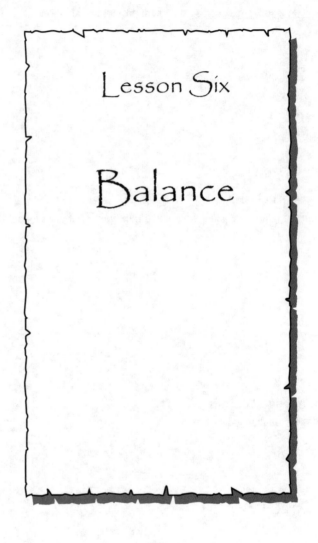

Lesson Six

Balance

The fifth basic principle

The next principle on our list is the principle of **Continuous Motion.** Long ago, T'ai Chi wasn't called T'ai Chi, it was called Chang Ch'uan, or Long Boxing. The name implied that it took a "long" time to complete the routine and, while practicing, the routine should appear to be one long continuous movement, rather than a series of little ones. Another name for T'ai Chi was "Yellow River Boxing," a name which again implied that the movements of T'ai Chi should flow together in one long continuous stream — like the Yellow River — twisting, coiling, changing direction, but yet always moving, always flowing, from headwaters to mouth, from beginning to end. Although you've been learning the movements one by one, when practicing the whole set, the movements should flow together continuously without any break in between.

Step Up
and Kick-right

1. Turn the waist slightly to the right, simultaneously, cross the hands by placing left hand, palm up, on the back of right wrist.

2. Step diagonally with the left foot into the 8 o'clock corner, slowly shifting forward forming a left bow step. At the same time separate the hands

3. Circle each hand outward and downward until they cross again, with the back of left hand against the inside of right wrist.

4. At the same time, bring right foot to the side of left foot and rest its toes on floor, T-step.

5. Look to the 10 o'clock corner raise the right leg, bent at the knee.

6. Thrust the right foot gradually forward towards 10 o'clock. At the same time, separate the hands, extending them sideways at shoulder level, with elbows slightly bent and palms turned outward. Look at your right hand.

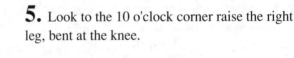

Box Both Ears

1. Pull back the right foot and bend the knee so that the thigh is level. At the same time, fold both arms in by bending the elbows to 45 degrees so that both palms are facing inward.

2. Brush both hands down in a curve to either side of right knee, palms up.

3. Look straight ahead, and step down with the right foot, into the 10 o'clock corner landing softly on the heel. At the same time, lower your hands to your sides.

4. Gradually clench the fists. as you shift your weight forward to form a bow step, circle the fists up and forward to eye level, coming toward each other in a pincers movement.

Just remember to keep your elbows down as much as possible -- this keeps your shoulders relaxed and protects your own body. In the final position, the first knuckles point to each other, backs of the hands facing you.

Step Up
and Kick-left

To get from the end of Box Both Ears to this next position, you will use the double weight shift, form T-step transition.

1. Rock back, and open both fists so that the palms face outward, fingers pointing to each other.

2. As you turn left and shift your weight to the left leg, separate the left hand away from the right. Turn your right toes to 8 o'clock.

3. Now shift your weight back to the right foot.

3. Step into a T-step with the left foot, crossing the left hand under the right. Turn left to face the four o'clock corner.

5. Raise the left knee.

6. Pulling back on the toe, slo-o-owly kick the left heel into the 4 o'clock corner. The left palm strikes into the same corner along with the kick. The right palm separates behind the right shoulder,into the 8 o'clock corner.

Exercises

1. If you're like most beginning students, you probably found it challenging to stand on one leg and kick out into the air. Many people tell me that the reason they don't learn T'ai Chi is because they don't have the balance for it. But this is a backwards view of learning T'ai Chi. T'ai Chi Ch'uan *teaches* you to develop balance, and in fact if you practice the beginners' version of Step Up and Kick every day your physical body will change remarkably.

Exercise: Stand up and shift your weight to the right leg. Put your awareness in the sole of your foot, and feel the complete weight of your body on it. Now shift over to the left foot. Feel the weight. Shift back to the right, feel the weight, and slowly lift the left foot. Now put the foot down, shift the weight to the left foot, and slowly lift the right foot. Once again, shift the weight slowly to the right foot, then lift the left foot up and finally straighten the left knee, extending the left foot out about shin high. Repeat again on the other side.

2. It's important to coordinate the extension of the arms with the kicking action of the legs. The arms extend into each corner. In other words, when the right foot kicks to 10 o'clock, one arm extends to 10 o'clock and the other arm extends to 8 o'clock. Moreover, the arms extend simultaneously with the kick.

Try this exercise: Step 1 _Stand facing 9 o'clock, and make a V with your arms to both corners. Now soften elbows by bending them slightly.

Step 2 —Cross your wrists at the hip level. Now lift them up to chest level, turn the palms out and extend them in a V to each corner.

Step 3 —Cross your wrists at the chest level. Turn the palms out, and circle the hands out away from each other, crossing them at the wrists again at hip level. Now lift them up to chest level, turn the palms out and extend them in a V to each corner. Make some notes below.

Practice Notes & Performance Analysis

I. Solution Analysis:
Write a <u>first person, present tense</u> statement providing a solution.

II. Success Analysis:
Write something positive about what you did in practice or class today.

III. Knowledge Analysis:
"What did I learn <u>new</u> today?"

Lesson Seven

Flexibility

The sixth basic principle

    The sixth basic principle of T'ai Chi is to **Balance Yin and Yang**. When you follow the principle of Continuous Motion, you keep both the blood and the ch'i circulating. But that principle also has a deeper, philosophical meaning. Most people have seen the yin and yang symbol, a circle divided by a wavy line, one half light and one half dark. Yin and yang are often defined as the pair of positive and negative, but that's not really an accurate definition. Yin and yang are really better defined as "this and that," two opposite and equal mirror images of one thing. At the heart of most Asian religious and philosophical beliefs is the principle of Yin and Yang, and as we see in this drawing, the ideal state — the natural state — is for Yin and Yang to be in perfect balance.

    T'ai Chi was designed to be a physical representation of harmony. The T'ai Chi movements should all show a balance of force and direction. This symbol also shows that there is more to the relationship of Yin and Yang than just balance there is also movement. According to the ancient Chinese philosophers, the universe is constantly in motion, like a wheel, ever changing from one extreme state to another. Moreover, the direction of change is from one state to the other and back again. The wheel never stops turning, and the progression from yin to yang never comes to a rest. All kinds of opposites are paired: Left and right, up and down, as well as easy and difficult. The wheel of change never stops. In the same way, the movements of your T'ai Chi form are always changing from one extreme to another and back again.

Snake Creeps Down-left

1. Fold in the left leg so that the knee is bent and the thigh is even with the floor.

2. Reach out with the right hand towards 9 o'clock and form a right hook hand. Meanwhile, left palm is folded in and placed in front of right shoulder. (This posture should look just like Single Whip.)

3. Step back with the left foot landing toe first to create a bow step, right foot forward.

4. Turn to the left to six o'clock, turning the right toes inward. Open up the left foot until the toes point to 3 o'clock. Now, crouch slowly on you right leg. As you sink down, the Snake -- I mean the left hand —circles down toward your right knee. Leave the right hand hooked hand behind you.

5. Now shift your weight to the left foot by pushing yourself forward from the right foot. Your right leg straightens and your left leg bends to form a bow step with the left foot forward. At the same time, your left hand reaches forward toward 3 o'clock.

Rooster Stands on One Leg-right

S nake Creeps Through the Grass and Rooster Stands on One Leg should follow each other so closely that they should appear to be part of the same long movement.

1. Step up slowly into a T-step, extending the supporting left leg. Open the hook hand and swing the palm forward, past your right hip, to the front.

2. Raise your right knee, and lift the right hand until your bent elbow is just above right knee, fingers pointing up and palm facing outward. Lower your left hand to the side of your left hip, palm down. In the final position, look through the notch between the thumb and forefinger of your right hand.

Snake Creeps Down-right

1. Turn body to the left.

2. At the same time, raise your left hand sideways to shoulder level and form a hook hand. The right hand, following body turn, moves in a curve until it comes in front of left shoulder with fingers pointing up. Look at left hand.

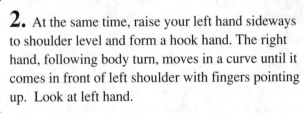

3. Step back diagonally with the right foot landing toe first to create a bow step, left foot forward.

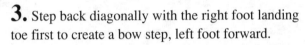

4. Turn to the right, turning the left toes inward. Crouch slowly on left leg. As you sink down, the right hand lowers to the floor by your left knee. Leave the left hook hand behind you.

5. Now shift your weight to the right foot. The left leg straightens and right leg bends to form a bow step with the right foot forward. At the same time, right arm continues to extend forward. The hook hand is still in the same spot, behind you.

MOVEMENT NINETEEN
Rooster Stands on One Leg-left

1. Step up slowly into a T-step. Open the hook hand and swing the palm forward to the front.

2. Raise the left knee, and lift the left hand until the bent elbow is just above left knee, fingers pointing up and palm facing leftward. Lower the right hand to the side of right hip, palm down. Look at your left hand.

Exercises

1. Snake Creeps Down requires flexibility, right? Wrong! Snake Creeps Down *improves* flexibility through daily practice. You must, however, start by keeping your body in the correct alignment -- and then by degrees you can sink down lower and lower.

To help you practice the correct posture, you can use a normal kitchen chair. Try this: Sit down on the corner of the chair *on one cheek only.* Leave the leg opposite the cheek you're sitting on stretched out a little, knee still slightly bent. Relax. No, I mean *really* relax. Now stand up just enough to clear the chair. This is the correct posture -- and probably the correct beginner's height -- for this movement. Practice making this posture 5-6 times on each cheek. Make some notes below.

2. The fifth basic principle is the principle of Continuous Motion. The continuous, uninterrupted flow of movements in the T'ai Chi Ch'uan routine is a model for the continuous circulation of your ch'i. Snake Creeps Down should flow smoothly from the end of Step Up and Kick to the end of Rooster Stands on One Leg.

The movement is almost like ducking under a waist high fence wire. First extend your leg under the wire. Then duck down on your side, away from the wire. Push yourself under the fence, shifting your weight from rear to front, and then stand up.

Holding this image in your mind, review the movements of Snake Creeps Down through Rooster Stands on One Leg, focusing on the principle of Continuity. Make some notes below.

Practice Notes & Performance Analysis

I. Solution Analysis:
Write a <u>first person, present tense</u> statement providing a solution.

II. Success Analysis:
Write something positive about what you did in practice or class today.

III. Knowledge Analysis:
"What did I learn <u>new</u> today?"

Lesson Eight

Reviewing
the
Principles

Fair Lady Works Shuttles

1. From the end of Rooster Stands on One Leg, turn to the left and step down into the 2 o'clock corner, creating a T-step with the weight on the left foot, and hold the ball, left hand on top.

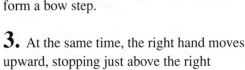

2. Step diagonally with the right foot into the 4 o'clock corner to form a bow step.

3. At the same time, the right hand moves upward, stopping just above the right temple with the palm turned obliquely upward (a blocking move).

4. The left hand pushes forward and upward to nose level, palm facing forward (a palm strike).Fair Lady Works Shuttles is a two-step movement. To get to the next position, use the rock back, rock forward and step up to a t-step transition.

5. Rock back, lifting the right toe, and then immediately shift the weight forward and step up onto the right foot, making a T-step with the left foot. All the weight is on the right foot.

6. As you step up into your T-step, fold your hands in to hold the ball, this time right hand on top.

7. Step diagonally with the left foot into the 2 o'clock corner to create a Bow step.

8. At the same time, the left hand moves upward, stopping just above the left temple with the palm turned obliquely upward (a blocking move).

9. The left hand pushes forward and upward to the nose level, palm facing forward (2 palm strike).

Needle at the Sea Bottom

 o get to the next movement, use the Empty-step change transition.

1. Shift your weight forward onto the left foot, and  step up a half-step with the right foot. As you shift the weight back onto the right leg, completing the Empty-step change, turn your waist slightly to the right. Circle the arms (left hand over and right hand under) just as you did in Brush Knee. Shift all your weight back onto the right leg, which will create an Empty step.

Now, don't forget that while the feet are making the Empty step change, your hands are also moving.

2. When the right hand reaches the side of the right ear, turn back to the left, sink down on top of the right leg and thrust the right hand like a spear obliquely downward in front of the body, coming to rest by the side of the left knee. Replace the left foot to line up directly with 3 o'clock. In the final position, the body should be facing straight towards 3 o'clock. The left hand completes its motion by withdrawing to the left hip, palm down.

Exercises

1. List all six of the Six Basic Principles. (Try to do it without looking through the book.)

1.

2.

3.

4.

5.

6.

2. **Exercise:** Practicing the Principles
1. Pick a movement you know well—Part Horse's Mane, for example.
2. Repeat 8-10 steps of this movement, focusing on the first principle only—Slowing Down. Try to move as slowly as you can, keeping a consistent tempo.
3. Now repeat the 8-10 steps, this time focusing on just the second principle—Relaxing. Try to move as gently and softly as you can.
4. Repeat this procedure with each of the six other basic principles.

Lesson Nine

Finishing the Form

Open Arms Like a Fan

1. Take a step forward with left foot to form a Bow step.

2. At the same time, raise your right arm with the elbow bent until your hand stops just above right temple. Turn the right palm obliquely upward with the thumb pointing downward.

3. Raise your left hand slightly and push it forward at nose level with the palm facing forward. Look at the left hand, and open the waist towards the right.

As you step forward to perform this motion, the hands extend just as they did in Fair Lady Works Shuttles. The only difference is that previously, the striking palm was opposite the stepping foot. In this movement, however, the striking palm (left) is on the same side as the stepping foot.

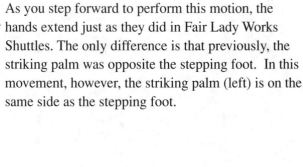

Deflect Downward, Parry and Punch

T o get to the next movement, use the double weight-shift to form a T-step transition. In fact, the transition here is the same as the transition between the two Grasp Bird's Tail movements.

1. From the end of Open Arms Like a Fan. turn right, and shift your weight to the right leg. This will allow you to turn your left toes to six o'clock.

2. Now shift your weight back to the left foot and step in with the right foot, T-step. At the very end of your transition, as you make that T-step, fold your right hand leftward and downward in a curve and then, with fingers clenched into fist, past abdomen to the side of left ribs.

3. Turn body to the right (9 o'clock) and step down onto the heel of the right foot.

Reverse View

Reverse View

4. As you step down, left hand presses down in front of the abdomen. This is Deflect Down. Simultaneously, the right fist also comes forward, over the top of the left elbow, as a backfist. This is Parry.

5. Pivoting on the heel, turn the toes of the right foot towards 12 o'clock. Meanwhile, pull the right fist in a curve back to the side of your right waist with knuckles turned downward. The left hand simply floats.

6. Staying slightly extended in front of the body, look at your left hand.

7. Step diagonally with the left foot to create a Bow step as right fist strikes forward (toward 9 o'clock) at chest level. Pull the left hand back to the side of the right forearm, and look at your right fist. This is Punch.

Closing the Door

---

1. Open the right fist.

2. Turn the left fingers to point down toward earth and slide the left hand under the right wrist and then past the open palm. Turn both palms up, separate your hands and pull them back slowly.

3. Rock back with toes of left foot raised, shifting weight on to right leg.

4. Turning palms down in front of chest, push them downward past abdomen and then up again as you shift forward.

5. As the weight shifts forward, bend the left leg to form a Bow step. The movement finishes with wrists at shoulder level, palms facing forward. Look between your hands.

6. Rock back, turn your body to the right as the toes of your left foot turn inward to face 12 o'clock.

7. As the body turns right, circle both hands outward, separating the right hand away from the left.

8. Shift the weight back to the left, circling the hands back together to cross again at the waist.

9. Turn the toes of the right foot inward to face 12 o'clock, then step in with the right foot towards left foot so that they are parallel and shoulder-width apart. Cross both hands at wrist in front of the chest.

10. Turn both palms down and separate them apart.

11. Gradually straighten both legs and slowly lower the hands to your sides. Look straight ahead.

Exercises

1. Check yourself on your recall:

List the Basic Positions

1.

2.

3.

4.

5. (Hint: this one's a hand position)

List the basic transitions

1.

2.

3.

4.

5.

2. Now that you have learned the whole form, all the basic principles, and all the details of movements -- forget them!

Take yourself to a special place -- a park, or up in the mountains, or to a secluded beach. Stand for a long time in the T'ai Chi position. Let your feet sink into the earth; let your head rise up to heaven. When you are ready, begin Open the Door... and then just let go. Whatever your body does is right -- even if it doesn't look like the Short Form. Just let go -- and let it flow!

Practice Notes & Performance Analysis

I. Solution Analysis:

Write a <u>first person, present tense</u> statement providing a solution.

II. Success Analysis:

Write something positive about what you did in practice or class today.

III. Knowledge Analysis:

"What did I learn <u>new</u> today?"